... is more important than your illness

Would you like it back?

Even if you're bedbound, depressed, chronically fatigued or unable to see or get about, this book will help.

If you've had a diagnosis that frightens you - that might even feel like a death sentence - or if you're struggling after years of impaired mobility, we have a way to help you feel a bit better each day.

It's all about understanding one truth: **you are bigger than your problems.** Which means that they needn't stop you doing things, experiencing things, loving, laughing, tasting and living your life. Yes, even if you can't get out of bed at the moment.

What you do is make changes to the way you think and act, creating a new relationship between your illness and yourself that separates *who you are* from *what you've got*.

Let's begin with a slice of pie...

If you imagine your life as a pie, how much of it is taken up by your illness do you think? Half? Three quarters? More?

If your illness is the biggest thing, this book will show you how to cut it down to size, shrinking it back until you see it for what it is - just one of the slices in the pie that is your life.

Page by page, you'll come across things to do and ways of thinking that will make your illness seem smaller.

In the first part of the book you'll write down the things that already help you feel better, then make a plan to enjoy more of them.

In the second half, we'll talk about 11 things that can have an effect on how ill you feel, and show you how to take control of them so that you feel better rather than worse.

Turn the page and let's get started with section 1!

IS THIS
HOW IT
FEELS?

THINK
ABOUT
A GOOD
DAY

If you're like most people, your illness isn't always at its worst.

There are some days (or parts of a day) when you feel a bit better. Nights when you get some sleep, times when you're so engrossed in something that you forget about your pain or your problem for a few hours or minutes.

So think about one of these times now – a time when your illness became a little smaller for some reason – and write down why you felt better in one of the empty pie slices over the page.

If there are more good times you can think of, keep writing about these in the other slices until the pie is full.

Got the idea? Then get your pencil and turn the page!

Write the good times in your pie

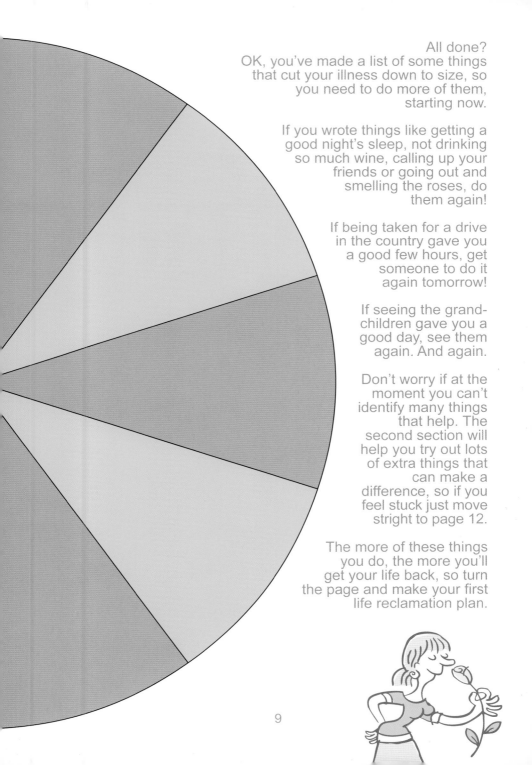

All done?
OK, you've made a list of some things
that cut your illness down to size, so
you need to do more of them,
starting now.

If you wrote things like getting a
good night's sleep, not drinking
so much wine, calling up your
friends or going out and
smelling the roses, do
them again!

If being taken for a drive
in the country gave you
a good few hours, get
someone to do it
again tomorrow!

If seeing the grand-
children gave you a
good day, see them
again. And again.

Don't worry if at the
moment you can't
identify many things
that help. The
second section will
help you try out lots
of extra things that
can make a
difference, so if you
feel stuck just move
stright to page 12.

The more of these things
you do, the more you'll
get your life back, so turn
the page and make your first
life reclamation plan.

LIFE
RECLAMATION
PLAN
NO.1

Look back at the things you wrote in the spaces on the pie and write them again here.

Now put the date you're going to do each one again here.

....

....

....

....

....

....

....

....

....

....

....

....

....

....

....

So that's your first plan and, because it's made up of things that you know make you feel better, it'll work.

You need to get started with it in about half an hour. Why not straight away? Because there's the rest of the book to read, remember?

11
STEPS
TO
FEELING
BETTER

(more or less guaranteed)

This part of the book is in 4-page sections and there are 11 of them. On the first two pages of each section we discuss one issue that may be preventing you from enjoying your life as much as you could.

Then, on the second two pages of each section we help you deal with the problem, usually with a list of things you could do **MORE** of, followed by another list you might want to do **LESS** of.

Some sections won't apply, of course. You may already be doing them perfectly, or you may not be physically able to do them. But if you work on all the things you *can* do, we guarantee you'll feel better.

It'll happen slowly at first, but as you follow your life reclamation plan and fix these 11 things as well, you'll begin to enjoy more and more good hours or days, and you really will feel as if you're getting your life back.

HERE ARE THE 11 THINGS WE'RE GOING TO WORK ON

1. The power of sleep
2. Doing stuff... but not too much
3. Enjoying things again
4. Ignoring your illness
5. A little knowledge…

now turn over and let's get some sleep!

THE
POWER
OF
SLEEP

Getting a good night's sleep has an amazing effect on how you feel, both mentally and physically.

It's like the best possible medicine, without side effects, prescriptions or visits to the chemist.

If you're sleeping badly, don't accept this as normal. Don't assume you can't do anything about it.

Whatever your illness or level of pain or stiffness, it's possible to improve your sleep and start to feel better all round.

When you turn the page, you'll see two lists – the do's and don'ts of sleeping better.

Some of them might seem a bit self-indulgent – a milky drink, a warm bath – but they really work and you do need to be good to yourself and put our suggestions into action.

DO MORE OF THIS

• Getting into a sleep routine.
Go to bed at the same time
every day

• Preparing for sleep with a warm, bubbly
bath and a milky drink

• Listening to soothing music just
before bedtime

• Fixing your bed if it's uncomfortable. Get
some new pillows or bedding,
or have someone turn the mattress

• Making your bedroom dark and
comfy. Get some thicker curtains
or even black-out blinds

• Making your bedroom warm and cosy but
not too hot. Add a duvet
if necessary.

• Making your bedroom lovely and
quiet. And if you live on a busy road,
get some ear-plugs!

DO LESS OF THIS

• Napping or snoozing during the day. You'll seize up and your pain may get worse. Keep sleep for bedtime.

• Staying in bed till late. Getting up in the morning helps you go to sleep at night.

• Drinking before bed. It feels as if it makes you sleepy, but it's just a shallow sleep and you may have to go to the loo halfway through the night.

• Reading or watching TV in bed. Don't do it at all - try to get to the stage where bed is just for sleeping.

• Exercising before bed. Getting physically tired might seem like a good idea, but actually it's not as good as slowly winding down. Don't do anything strenuous near bedtime.

• Tossing and turning. If you don't go to sleep within ten minutes, get up, go downstairs and read or watch TV until you feel sleepy and tired. Then try going to bed again.

• Worrying. Easy for us to say, but we're serious. If you're constantly turning worries over in your mind while in bed, get up and do it downstairs instead. Write them all down and plan to deal with them tomorrow. Then go to bed again.

DOING TOO MUCH (OR NOT ENOUGH)

Achieving things, including little things, is an important part of being alive. No-one can do nothing and feel happy about it.

At the same time, trying to do too much can also lead to problems, especially when you're ill, fatigued, physically weak or feeling down. The trick is what the professionals call 'pacing'. Doing something every day, but not to the point of exhaustion. Breaking tasks into chunks and working on them a little at a time.

If you're trying to get mobile again after a long period of rest, don't start with the London Marathon, but do set yourself a series of smaller targets and keep the momentum going.

Making progress towards a goal is one of the best things you can do to feel well. When it's a physical goal, it has the added benefit of building up your strength and fitness.

But always base your plans on what you can do now, not the things you used to do before you became ill. It's also a good idea to get your doctor's advice on a safe level of activity and a realistic target.

Use the do's and don'ts on the next two pages as a checklist to help get you going again.

DO MORE OF THIS

• Making activity plans with firm objectives – once round the garden, as far as the shops, to the loo by myself, back on the motorbike, walk to the park to see my chums – that kind of thing.

• Breaking the plan into chunks based on how you feel. Taking slow and steady steps towards your goal is the way to go.

• Knowing that you may need to stretch or massage out-of-practice muscles or even use pain-killers at first.

• Being realistic and prepared to stop or rest part way through.

• Asking for what you need – which may mean saying Can we only do half the distance this time?

• Consciously enjoying a sense of achievement after each small step towards your goal.

• Congratulating yourself when you have reached the target!

DO LESS OF THIS

• Listening to voices that say "You should be doing more than this".

• Setting unrealistic goals. It's perfectly OK to mow just part of the lawn today.

• Rushing through a task to get it out of the way. Slow down, break it into small pieces, do it on several different occasions and enjoy each part of it.

• Starting too fast - you're not running a marathon!

• Starting too slowly - you won't notice any changes.

• Doing lots of unplanned activities if you feel better one day – you may overdo it and spoil tomorrow.

• Regretting that you can't do as much as you used to. It gets you nowhere and stops you enjoying what you can do now.

BALANCING THE SHOULD STUFF WITH THE GOOD STUFF

When we're ill, we cut down on the things we do. It's only natural and sometimes it's unavoidable.

Trouble is, when choosing what activities to drop, we usually pick the ones we like! We keep doing the stuff we're supposed to for as long as possible – the work, the duties, the chores – but we tend to stop doing things that give us pleasure.

No wonder life seems grey and pointless.

To put some of the colour back into life, you need to re-visit the *good* stuff and maybe drop some of the *should* stuff.

Think about things that used to give you pleasure or a sense of achievement. Or things you thought were worthwhile or made you feel close to others.

Now use the next two pages and get your stuff balanced out!

THE GOOD STUFF I'M GOING TO GET BACK

Tick the things you used to enjoy but have stopped doing lately. Add some of your own at the end.

Watching or playing sport

Going out with friends

Listening to music

Going to movies/watching a film at home

Throwing parties or going to them

Phoning or texting friends

Laughing with friends

Going for a walk

Doing exercises

Joining societies or clubs

Learning to drive

Playing a musical instrument
Riding a bike or motorbike
Doing drama
Going to the church, temple, mosque or synagogue
Helping other people

....

....

....

....

....

....

....

....

....

....

Now pick two of these and add them to your reclamation plan on page 10. Choose a date to start doing them again.

IS YOUR ILLNESS ON YOUR MIND?

You are not your illness.

You are a person with ideas, values, hobbies, friends, opinions, memories. Your illness can't take any of that away.

But it tries! All illnesses love filling your consciousness, popping up in every thought or constantly lurking in the background.

It's a trick of the mind. If you've ever changed to a different car you'll have spotted that every other passing vehicle now seems to be the same as yours. When things are relevant to us, we notice them.

It's the same with illness.

Suddenly, every other TV programme or magazine article seems to be about your ailment, and when you watch or read them, your symptoms can seem worse and you feel every ache and pain.

The operative word in that last sentence was 'seem'. It's your thoughts that are focusing on your problems, making symptoms worse, and it's also your thoughts that can kick them into the long grass where they belong.

…with the help of the do's and don'ts on the next two pages.

DO MORE OF THIS

• Gather helpful information to work out what things make you feel better and worse.

• Thinking beyond your symptoms. Look through your illness to the outside world and really appreciate it.

• Recognising worrying thoughts and letting them be – Oh you're just my illness trying to muscle in on my thoughts – get back in your box!

• Defying your symptoms. If your illness says you can't do something, such as going to a party, ignore it and just go. You'll find that illnesses are often wrong.

• Staying focused on what you are doing or who you are with. When you're fully engaged and experiencing every second of your encounters and activities, your illness won't be able to get a thought in edgeways!

DO LESS OF THIS

• Don't just keep diaries and lists of symptoms for no reason. It just makes them seem more important than they are.

• Trying not to think about your illness. It never works. Instead, check the second point on the opposite page and just put the thought aside.

• Reading medical articles or searching online all the time. You need to know something about your illness, but putting all your efforts into trying to know everything can just stop you getting better.

• Answering in detail when people ask how you are. Get into the habit of just saying Fine! You could even tell your friends to stop saying How are you?

• Feeling or examining your body all the time. Once in a while is OK, but checking things every day just makes them seem worse.

• Constantly seeking reassurance – How do I look?

WHAT
DO
YOU
KNOW?

It's important to know about your illness, but it's not your job to be the world authority. You don't have the training and you don't have the time (you've got a life to lead, remember?)

So what's the right amount of knowledge for you?

Well, the National Institute for Clinical Excellence (NICE) is pretty good at telling it like it is, and all their information and advice is based on evidence, so you know it's tested, proven and reliable.

Just click onto www.nice.org.uk find the subject you're interested in and download the pdf's marked 'advice for patients and carers'.

Have a look at the next two pages before you get clicking, though.

DO MORE OF THIS

• Going to the local library and checking their Healthy Reading Scheme

• Using only credible information sources online such as www.patient.co.uk and www.nhs.uk

• Getting to know the doctor and trusted health practitioners in your area and making sure that you only deal with people who are accredited by a well known external body. The Health Professions Council, BABCP, BACP, BPS, UKCC, UKCP and the GMC in the UK are amongst the top ones.

• Linking up with the leading charity organisation that is concerned with your illness.

• Getting support from groups and chat rooms, but not to the exclusion of people and professionals that you see in the real world.

DO LESS OF THIS

• Believing everything you read online. Some of it is biased, commercial or plain wrong.

• Accepting every treatment or opinion as automatically correct. Would you trust an unqualified person's judgment about football or politics?

• Getting scared by stories of suffering or by something you read. Some illnesses will cause suffering and some will kill us, but there are thousands of treatments that cure or improve things.

• Losing faith in your own doctor. Proven, evidence-based health service treatments are still the gold standard.

• Trying all the latest treatment fads. If something works, you can bet **NICE** knows about it.

• Constantly monitoring your health. Check blood pressure, blood sugar or your weight if appropriate, but don't check all the time – it only focuses your mind on your illness rather than your life.

WHEN SAFETY ISN'T SENSIBLE

Some people don't go out unless they're carrying a mobile phone. Others will only go shopping with friends – not because they like to, but because they fear not having them there.

Some people avoid walking, not because they can't, but because they might fall and hurt themselves. Others take an extra couple of prescribed tablets to get through something scary, even when they weren't due to take them.

Although these things make us feel safer and more confident, it's usually a confidence trick. What we're doing is shrinking our lives by hiding the fact that we're scared.

Now, when you're ill, or have experienced a change in what you can do, being scared is understandable at first. But if you face your fears, you'll get part of your life back and your illness won't be able to take over more and more slices of your pie.

So here's what you do:

Think about what you do, how you do it, and what you could do if you weren't scared. Do any confidence tricks apply to you? If so, write them down on the next page.

Then, using the planner you'll see opposite your list, plan the 10 little steps you're going to take, to do the thing you're scared of.

cotton wool

MY LIFE WOULD BE BIGGER IF I WASN'T SO WORRIED ABOUT ...

(we've filled in some examples)

Meeting **new people**

Getting out **of bed**

Going out **alone**

Being in **crowded places**

Going back **to work**

Walking **somewhere I might fall**

....

....

....

....

....

Good list! Now choose one thing and write it twice on the planner page opposite.

Plan 10 tiny steps to beat your fear.

CAN'T..
(write the thing you chose in here)

Step 1 ....

Step 2 ....

Step 3 ....

Step 4 ....

Step 5 ....

Step 6 ....

Step 7 ....

Step 8 ....

Step 9 ....

Step 10 ....

CAN..
(write the thing you chose in here again)

TESTING, TESTING

What would you say if your doctor confessed to having learned everything she knows about your illness from the internet and newspapers? You'd be dismayed, wouldn't you? Or maybe outraged.

Happily, this is far from the truth. Every doctor has been through at least four years of study followed by more years of practice, and has access to medical journals and information that lay people simply never see.

So why do we seem occasionally to disbelieve our doctors? What makes us seek not just a second opinion, but a third and fourth, or more laboratory tests?

Well, sometimes, it's because our illness has become the focus of our life.

As we said on page 29, illnesses are good at this. They try to be in every thought, pop up in every conversation. And when they've got us good and hooked, they have us checking and feeling and sensing every twinge and tingle until we're sure there's something else the matter with us.

Now, sometimes, there is. But often, when we ask for test after test, it's sometimes because our illness has become bigger than our life.

Follow the do's and don'ts over the page to cut it down to size.

LATEST
HEALTH
SCARE

DO MORE OF THIS

• Realising that you and your doctor are a team and how you feel is your responsibility as well as your doctor's.

• Accepting expert diagnoses and advice.

• Asking questions without becoming obsessed.

• Trusting test results and investigations if your doctor is happy to trust them.

• Knowing when to stop looking for more opinions.

• Doing things to feel better each day rather than always trying to find out why you feel ill.

• Thinking about things outside your body. When you focus on trees or flowers or the task in hand, you don't feel your aches and pains quite so much.

• Taking prescribed medication exactly as prescribed

DO LESS OF THIS

• Constantly seeking another opinion (one or two is usually enough). Sure, seek a second opinion – but know when to stop.

• Obsessing about your illness with too much online research.

• Demanding test after test even when they come back negative.

• Constantly worrying that your doctor is missing something.

• Focusing so much on your body or emotions that you always feel there's something wrong, somewhere.

• Reading sensational press or online comment about hospitals, doctors, diets or cures.

• Taking alternative or self-chosen medication instead of what your doctor has prescribed.

RUTS
AND
ROUTINES

The less you do, the worse you feel.

"Hang on!" You're saying, "I'm ill, of course I'm doing less!" And that's a perfectly reasonable response.

But sometimes, you can get into a rut of doing very little. This is a shame, because you'd feel a lot better (and your life would get a lot bigger) if you created an activity routine.

Now, no-one is suggesting anything too strenuous, so don't turn the page yet. Instead, we think you should decide to do something that uses your mind and, if you're able, your muscles, at regular intervals throughout the day, every day.

This will do three things: it'll get you awake with a purpose and a plan, it'll stimulate your mind and muscles so that you don't feel as poorly, and it'll kick your illness off more slices of your pie.

Good value? Of course!

Now turn over for... well, you know the routine by now.

DO MORE OF THIS

• Taking on chores and responsibilities. Volunteer to walk the dog, take the children to school, water the flowers!

• Getting started at a set time. You'll be amazed how much better you feel when your day begins properly.

• Involving others in your routine. Ring your mum each morning, walk with a friend every Wednesday.

• Making your routine important. Choose something every day and commit to getting out of bed to do it.

• Enjoying the achievement when a daily job is done.

• Knowing the difference between aches and pains. Muscles and joints you haven't used for a while may ache at first. But if you're in pain, you must slow down. Pace things and seek the advice of your doctor.

• Challenging your unhelpful thoughts if they say you should be doing more, or you shouldn't do so much. Remember pacing (page 21).

DO LESS OF THIS

• Staying in bed on cold mornings. Remember, the less you do the worse you feel, the worse you feel, the less you do.

• Allowing your routine to slip after a few days. It takes a couple of weeks to really feel better, so stick it out!

• Letting yourself off the hook because you're having a bad day today. Routines make you feel good – they help to fix bad days!

• Choosing things that are too hard to do. What we're after is regular activities, not superhuman struggling.

• Choosing things that don't stretch you at all. "Every morning, I will eat a biscuit and go back to sleep" may be a routine, but it doesn't count!

• Listening to well-meaning friends or relatives that want to do everything for you.

LOOK FITTER, FEEL FITTER

The way we breathe and hold our bodies says a lot about how we're feeling, not only to other people, but also to ourselves.

Although it's reasonable to be hunched up or move tentatively when you're ill or in pain, these postures can become a habit and slow your progress towards feeling better.

It's an old cliché, we know, but the very act of smiling makes you feel happier as well as look happier. It's the same with sitting and standing. Straighten up and you'll look and feel less ill.

Walking, too, if you're able to do it, can be a good way to send a signal to yourself and other people. Try to walk a little straighter and faster. Try to limp a little less. Try not to hold on to the furniture or a stick so much. Walk more like a well person and you'll feel more like a well person.

There are some more ideas over the page.

DO MORE OF THIS

• Stretching your muscles in the morning, so that you're not so stiff.

• Massaging the bits of you that ache, so that you have less pain and can sit or stand more naturally.

• Asking loved ones to comment on your posture – you may not realise that you're so tensed up.

• Holding your head higher and looking straight ahead, not down.

• Breathing with your diaphragm, not your chest. This relaxes your upper body and can also help you feel less stressed.

Here's how you do it:

Sit or lie comfortably, with loose garments.

Put one hand on your chest and one on your stomach.

Slowly inhale through your nose or through pursed lips (to slow down the intake of breath).

As you inhale, feel your stomach expand with your hand and try to keep your chest still.

Slowly exhale through pursed lips to regulate the release of air.

Feel your stomach contract as you exhale and try to keep your chest still.

Practice until it becomes natural. Try to make this your normal way of breathing.

DO LESS OF THIS

• Doing too much all at once.
Leaping from the top of the wardrobe
may not be appropriate just yet!.

• Grunting and groaning when you get up
or sit down. You may not realise that you
do it, but when you stop, you'll sound more
agile and also feel this way, too.

• Breathing fast and shallow. This tenses
your upper body and can also make you
feel upset.

• Taking tiny, frightened steps. Step out a
little more boldly, with a stick if necessary,
and look straight ahead.

• Protecting yourself with your arms,
or always holding part of your body.
It's natural when in pain, but can become
a habit.
Try to loosen up and straighten out – you'll
look and feel better.

ARE YOU INSIDE OUT?

When you're ill, it's not unusual
to withdraw from the world.
You don't want visitors. You push
people away. Your thoughts focus
inside, on your aches and pains
and how you're feeling
this morning.

Eventually, you may not even
bother opening the curtains.
The outside world - even on a
sunny day - seems miles away.

Trouble is, this sort of thing
just makes your illness bigger.
The more you look inside yourself,
the more your illness steals slices
of your pie.

The answer is to re-connect.
To look outside yourself.
To appreciate friends, family and
flowers again.

Try the do's and don'ts on the next
two pages and you'll soon see
what we mean!

DO MORE OF THIS

• Getting up or waking each morning and deliberately welcoming the day. Open the curtains, say hello, notice the weather and the view from your window.

• Calling up friends and family who may have stopped visiting. Asking to see them again – they'll be delighted!

• Going for walks (or being taken) and really noticing the world, the shops, the people, the trees. Walking with a friend is even better, of course.

• Setting a goal that involves other people – visit an old friend, go to the park and watch children playing, go to church, temple, synagogue or mosque again.

• Playing music. Music cheers you up and you feel more able to change. But don't play sad stuff. Keep it upbeat and you'll get an instant lift.

• Helping someone. Do a small kindness for someone else, every day, and you'll feel even better than they do.

DO LESS OF THIS

• Thinking about your symptoms. There's plenty of time for that when seeing the doctor. Right now, you've got a life to lead!

• Checking your body for aches and pains. You'll have some, that's a certainty, but focusing on them only makes them bigger.

• Refusing visitors. Other people help you feel better – even if you don't feel like it at the moment! You can always ask them to leave after a while.

• Grumbling. It's rotten being ill, but being miserable only makes it worse.

• Vegetating. Dozing, staring into space or watching daytime TV all day are all guaranteed to make you feel bad.

• Ignoring the day or the date. Being part of the world again means knowing what day it is! Connect with what's happening around you with newspapers and the radio.

HELPING YOUR HELPERS TO GET IT RIGHT

(ask them to read this bit, too)

Hello helper!
Thanks for reading this.

A helper's job includes understanding, listening and some practical stuff.

First, please have a look through the rest of the book and get to know what we're suggesting.

You'll spot that some things can't be done alone. There's help needed with walking, trips out, daily routines – so get ready to be called on for some of that!

Also, you'll need to polish up your listening skills so that you can really help when talking about feelings and plans.

You might want to do a bit of research, too. Reading about the illness online or getting some books out of the library will help you understand the situation and be even more useful.

Supporting someone sounds straightforward, but it isn't always. You may get irritated or frustrated. You may say or do things that you think are helpful, but don't seem to work. It's even possible to sometime make things worse without realising it.

But don't get discouraged. Over the page are the do's and don'ts of helping.

DO MORE OF THIS

- 'Being there' long term.

- Being willing to talk and offer support when needed.

- Being happy to help with household and other chores.

- Encouraging your friend or relative to make their reclamation plan and stick to it.

- Having a sense of humour and using it to help your friend or relative cope.

- Staying positive but realistic – things may get better, but there are no quick fixes. Sometimes they get worse, but being there throughout will help.

- Offering praise – I can see how you've worked hard at that.

- Helping your friend to pace things – he or she will get better bit by bit and mustn't take on too much, too soon.

- Staying well yourself by taking time out and getting advice from your doctor or a counsellor if necessary.

- Encouraging your friend or relative to seek extra help when needed.

DO LESS OF THIS

• Wrapping your friend or relative in cotton wool. You mustn't take over everything.

• Bullying or nagging. Advice is great. Constantly telling your friend or relative what to do, isn't.

• Shouting. If you feel frustrated with the way things are going, imagine how a poorly person feels. Stay calm.

• 'Being there' too much. Yes, it's possible. If your friend or relative is always on the phone to you or feels unable to cope without constantly getting reassurance, they've become addicted to you.
Try withdrawing and doing slightly less.

• Being unrealistic. Too many breezy statements like 'you'll be fine – don't worry!' or 'everything will work out!' eventually can make it seem as if you're not taking things seriously.

• Avoiding the issue. Problems need to be talked about, so don't let your friend or relative bottle things up for too long. Gently encourage opening up, but don't force things.

ARE YOU READY TO RECLAIM YOUR LIFE?